ピラン<ruby>奏<rt>かな</rt></ruby>でる シンフォニー

The Symphony of Piran

文・写真 <ruby>青山<rt>あおやま</rt></ruby> <ruby>英孝<rt>ひでたか</rt></ruby>

デザイン・編集 かわもと わかな

英訳 Derrick Copley

夏のある晴れた日
砦の頂上から海を眺めている
少年がいる。

かつて栄えたベネチア帝国の
侵入をしっかりと防いだ城跡が
街並みをやさしく包み込むように
そびえ立っているのが見える。

On a perfect summer's day, a boy looked out at sea from
the top of a fort.

The towering remains of the fort once protected
the Republic of Venice and gently enveloped the town
below.

眼下には屋根瓦がオレンジ畑のように広がっている。
先端の塔はまるでアドリア海を見張っているかのようだ。
青々とした海原が強い陽射しに照らされて輝いている。
少年は丘にそびえる教会に視線を移し、じっと眺めた。
鐘楼には眺めを楽しむ人々がかすかに見える。

He could see a vast sea of roof tiles from the houses below which looked almost like a field of oranges.
The tower at the very end of the fort kept watch over the Adriatic Sea.
The great blue sea shimmered under the hot summer sun.
The boy looked away from the sea and towards a church atop a hill.
He could just make out people enjoying the view in the bell tower.

聖堂の十字架の上に
1羽の海鳥が
羽を広げてひと休みしている。

On the cross above the church, a seabird rested,
stretching its wings.

その右側を見渡すと、
トリエステの街並みがはっきりと
姿を見せている。

To the right, the town of Trieste could clearly be seen.

少年は
潮風が通り抜ける鐘楼で
大きな双眼鏡をじっと
覗き込む人たちを見つけた。

The boy entered the bell tower through which
sea air was blowing.
He found people looking through big binoculars.

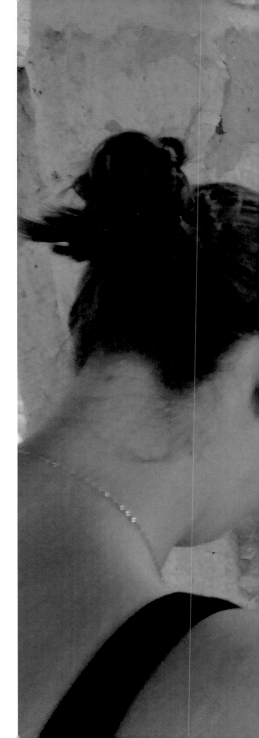

彼らはそれぞれ双眼鏡を手に持ち
周りの海の様子をていねいに
観察している。

少年は、彼らの視線を追うように
鏡のような穏やかな海に
そっと視線をおいた。

They held the binoculars in their hands and carefully surveyed
the surrounding sea.
The boy looked out at the mirror-like peaceful sea as if following
the eyes of those with the binoculars.

トロール漁船の背後に、
無数の海鳥が餌を求めて元気に飛び交っている。
辺りを見回すと、5隻のトロール船の背後にも同じ光景が見えた。
そのとき、
トロール船の背後に、2頭のイルカが元気よく姿を現した。

A countless number of birds were flying energetically around a fishing trawler, vying for food. Looking around, the boy could see five other trawlers also surrounded by birds.

In front of the scene, two dolphins jumped joyfully in and out of the water.

網から逃れた多くの魚を狙っているのだろう。
トロール船の後方に付いて泳いだり、網の周りを縫うように潜ったりしている。
少年はイルカの泳ぐ姿を興味深く眺めた。

He thought that they must be vying for the fish that escaped the nets.

They swam around the nets behind the fishing trawlers, as though knitting the edges of the nets.

The boy was fascinated by the scene of the swimming dolphins.

次の日、少年は街の小さな水族館に出かけた。
そこで、背びれを切り取られて泳ぐ
痛ましい姿のイルカを見つけた。

The next day, the boy went to the town's small aquarium.
There, he saw the tragic sight of a dolphin swimming with a cut down its back.
It seemed that it was cut by the propellor of a motor boat.

岸辺に打ち上げられた
イルカの亡骸もあった。

汚れた海がイルカの命を
脅かしていたのだ。

There was also a dead dolphin that had been washed ashore.
It was poisoned by the dirty ocean water.

大きな網がからだに絡まった無残なイルカも見つけた。
身動きがとれずに苦しかっただろう。

Furthermore, he saw a dolphin that was stuck in a massive net.
It seemed so distressed in a state of shock and couldn't move.

水質の悪化は寄生虫のはたらきを活発にした。
皮膚の大きな傷跡が痛々しかった。

The dirty water had contributed to the growth of parasites.
The scars and marks on its skin looked painful.

少年は心を痛めた。

楽しそうに泳ぐイルカたち
痛ましい姿のイルカたち

どちらのイルカも
同じピランの海で
生まれ育ったはずなのに...。

The boy felt hurt.
Dolphins frolicking in the sun and dolphins
in pain...
Such different destinies - even
though all of these dolphins
were born and raised in the
same seas of Piran.

少年の知っているピランの海
澄んだ海中を魚の群れが悠々と泳ぐユートピア
それは、少年が毎日見ているピランの日常であった。

誰かのおかげで美しい海を取り戻せたのだろうか。
少年は今感じる幸せと、湧き上がる疑問に
胸が張り裂けそうになった。

The Piran seas that the boy knew of were a utopia full of schools of fish swimming
calmly through clear waters.
That was the everyday Piran that he knew and loved.
Was someone able to bring back this beautiful sea?
The boy's heart nearly broke with the conflicting happiness and concern.

そのとき、どこからか心地よいシンフォニーが少年の耳に
聴こえてきた。タルティーニ広場からだ。
フルートやバイオリン、トランペットやティンパニなど、
どの楽器もそれぞれの音域がしっかりと響いている。

その美しい共鳴を、地元の人も旅人も、広場に佇む猫も
楽しそうに聴いている。

Just then, the boy started to hear a lovely symphony.It was coming from Tartini Square. Flutes, violins, trumpets and timpanis - the sound of every instrument was strongly reverberating across the town.

Everyone from local people and tourists, to the cats relaxing in the square were enjoying the beautiful melody.

少年はその時、
うつむいた顔を勢いよく青空に向け、そして、微笑んだ。
それぞれの音が美しく輝くことで、新たな響きが生まれている。
その新たな響きが、新たな感動となって届いてきたのだ。
きっと人間も、動物も、植物も、そして、海の生き物も、
同じように輝けるはず...。

At that moment, the boy stopped looking down, and looked up at the sky, with a smile.

Noticing that each individual musical note made a new sound that somewhat shined one more beautiful than the next and evoked powerful emotions to all that could hear.

He thought that surely humans, animals, plants and sea creatures could all shine in the same way.

寝そべって
日光浴を楽しむ人

People lying down in the sun.

クルーザーで
大海原を楽しむ人

The people that enjoy the
expansive sea from a boat.

潮風を浴びて
食事を楽しむ人

People eating while enjoying
the sea breeze.

海辺で美しい海を
楽しむ人

People enjoying the sea from
the coast.

滑らかな海原を楽しそうに疾走するイルカ

Dolphins swimming fast through the calm sea.

驚くような高さまで飛び跳ねるイルカ

Dolphins jumping high.

動物や植物がますます輝きを増している。

Animals and plants shining even brighter.

美しい自然に包まれ誰もが微笑んでいる。

Surrounded by beautiful nature, everyone was smiling.

ふるさとの海でイルカも躍動している。

The dolphins are also fully enjoying themselves in their home waters.

今朝も海の生き物を守ろうと、ピランを出航する。

That morning, the boy set sail from Piran to protect the creatures of the sea.

少年は思う。そして、心から願う。
生きとし生けるものすべてが仲良く、そして輝ける地球を …。

He thought to himself and prayed from his heart;

That all things that live, can live harmoniously to create a world that shines.

親子が響かせるハーモニーのように
ピランから世界を包み込んだシンフォニーを奏でたい。

In the like of the harmonious sounds made from a mother dolphin to its calve. He thought that he wanted to have a symphony that starts in Piran and encourages the whole world to join in.

人は美しいものに憧れる。
ありのままを慈しみ、輝く姿に共感すれば、
その美しさに魅せられるだろう。

People long for what is beautiful.
If we can love things the way they are and be grateful for
how they shine, We will all be taken by the beauty.

あなたも少年のように
ピランの街に恋をしてみませんか。

Why not fall in love with Piran, just as the boy did.

Hvala!
Piran, Slovenija
スロベニア共和国 ピラン

ピランで奏でるシンフォニー

2018年12月13日　　初版発行

文・写真　青山 英孝（あおやま ひでたか）

デザイン・編集　かわもと わかな

英訳　Derrick Copley（でりっく こぷり）

定価（本体価格1,700円＋税）

発行所　株式会社 三恵社
〒462-0056　愛知県名古屋市北区中丸町2-24-1　TEL 052-915-5211　FAX　052-915-5019
URL http://www.sankeisha.com

ISBN978-4-86487-950-7 C8739 ¥1700E